My Best Friends Are Dinosaurs

MY BEST FRIENDS ARE DINOSAURS

VERSE by
HOWARD KLEIN
PICTURES by
WINDROW

DAVID McKAY COMPANY, INC. NEW YORK

To

Adam and Lawrence

MY BEST FRIENDS ARE DINOSAURS

My best friends are dinosaurs,
I love their scaly necks.

My favorite ones are Bronty
And Tyrannosaurus Rex.

I love the Trachodon's duck-bill,

And Dimetrodon's high sail;

Triceratops's three head horns,

And Stegosaur's sharp tail.

Diplodocus just swims in swamps
And eats up slimy things;

While Pterodactyl overhead
Flies round on leather wings.

Kronosaur likes swimming too,
He's always chasing fish.

He snaps his jaws at Ichthyosaurs,
They make a tasty dish.

Ankylosaurus fights on land,
He's twenty-five feet long.

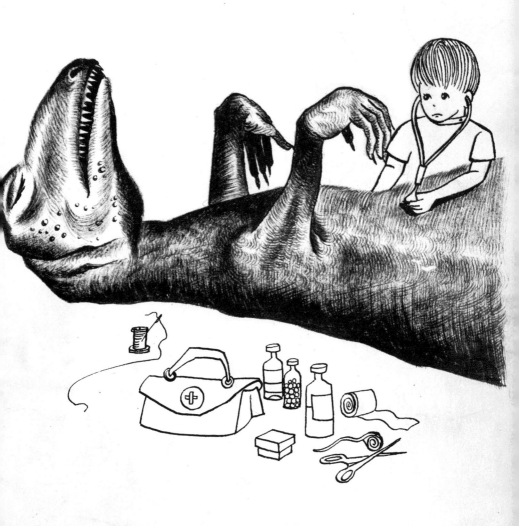

He'll kill an Allosaurus dead,
His club-tail is so strong.

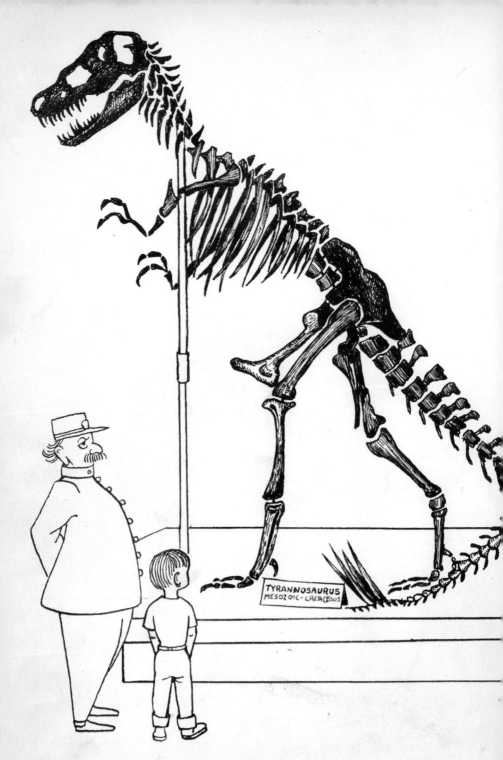

The dinosaurs are all gone now,
So says my friend, guard Max.

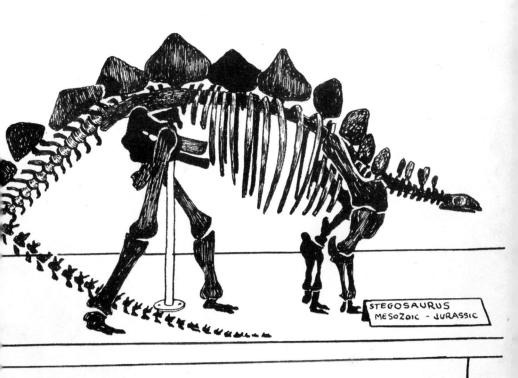

STEGOSAURUS
MESOZOIC - JURASSIC

They roamed one-hundred million years,
And all they left were tracks.

They didn't build big buildings,

They didn't paint or dance.

They didn't play in orchestras,

Or even go to France.

They weren't smart like people
Or else they'd be here yet.

But they were much, much bigger,
And lots more fun I'll bet.

Yes, my best friends are dinosaurs,
I love their scaly necks.

My favorite ones are Bronty,

And Tyrannosaurus Rex.

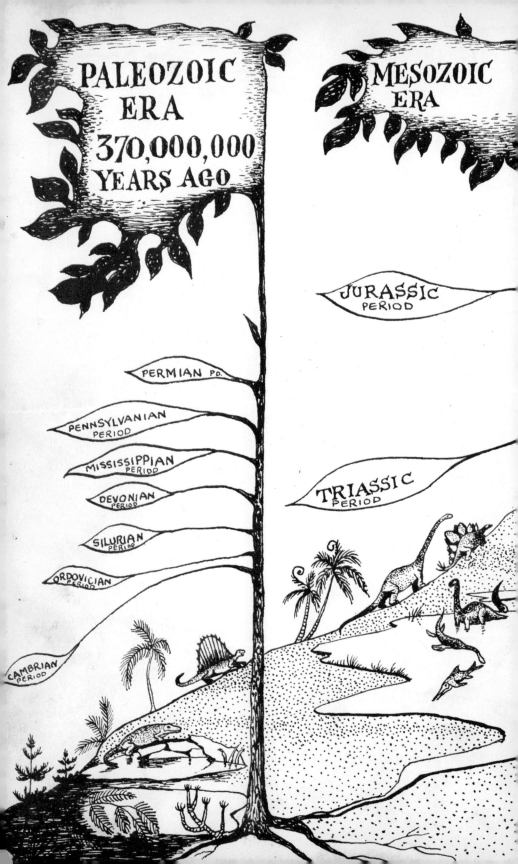

PALEOZOIC
ERA
370,000,000
YEARS AGO

MESOZOIC
ERA

JURASSIC
PERIOD

PERMIAN PD.

PENNSYLVANIAN
PERIOD

MISSISSIPPIAN
PERIOD

DEVONIAN
PERIOD

TRIASSIC
PERIOD

SILURIAN
PERIOD

ORDOVICIAN
PERIOD

CAMBRIAN
PERIOD

How to say the dinosaurs' names: